SHRUBS

1 Ceanothus Burkwoodii
○ E

Attractive rich blue flowers in July-October.

2 Ceanothus dentatus
○ E

Bushy erect habit. Bright blue flowers May-June.

3 Chaenomeles x superba 'Crimson and Gold'
○ ◑

Fruit suitable for jelly. Flowers March-May.

4 Chaenomeles x superba 'Pink Lady' *(Quince or Japonica)*
○ ◑

Charming variety. Flowers March-May.

5 Clematis 'Hagley Hybrid'
○

Elegant satin pink flowers June-September. Vigorous.

6 Clematis 'Jackmanii Superba'
○

Spectacular climber. Flowers borne in great profusion July-October.

7 Clematis 'Marie Boisselot' *(syn. Madame Le Coultre)*
○

Free flowering variety. Large pure white blooms June-Septmeber.

8 Clematis montana 'Alba' *(Grandiflora)*
○ ◑

Vigorous climber, excellent for growing in trees. Flowers May-June.

9 Clematis montana rubens
○ ◑

Flowers May-June. Strong growing variety. Ideal for covering unsightly outbuildings.

10 Clematis 'Nelly Moser'
○

Popular variety. Suitable for a north facing wall. Superb display of flowers May June and again August-September.

○	Full Sun
◑	Semi shade
●	Shade tolerating
E	Evergreen
PP	Prefers peat

All sizes quoted are a general guide but depend upon area, growing conditions and trimming.

WALL/CLIMBING SHRUBS

1 **Clematis 'Rouge Cardinale**
○

Bright crimson velvety coloured flowers June-August.

2 **Clematis 'The President'**
○

Purple-blue flowers with silver reverse June-September. Very reliable.

3 **Clematis tangutica**
○

Lantern-like flowers and feathery seed heads.

4 **Clematis 'Ville de Lyon'**
○

Carmine-red flowers, late June-September. Looks delightful sprawling over an arch.

5 **Clematis 'Vyvyan Pennell'**
○

Fully double blooms are produced from May-July. Single flowers from August-September.

6 **Cotoneaster horizontalis**
(Fish Bone Cotoneaster)
○ ◑ ● E

Wide spreading. Coral-red berries clothe the glossy foliage in Autumn.

7 **Garrya elliptica**
(Silk Tassel Bush)
○ ◑ E

Produces decorative catkins January-February.

8 **Hedera colchica 'Dentata Variegata'**
(Ivy)
○ ◑ ● E

An attractive form. Self-clinging.

9 **Hedera colchica 'Paddy's Pride'**
(Ivy)
○ ◑ ● E

A handsome variegated ivy. Self-clinging.

10 **Hedera helix 'Goldheart'**
(Ivy)
○ ◑ ● E

Superb ivy with bright leaves with striking yellow central splash.

○	Full Sur
◑	Semi shade
●	Shade tolerating
E	Evergreer
PP	Prefers pea

All sizes quoted are a general guide but depend upon area, growing conditions and trimming.

WALL/CLIMBING SHRUBS

1 **Hedera helix 'Hibernica'**
(Irish Ivy)

○ ◐ ● E

Vigorous with bold dark green leaves.

2 **Hydrangea petiolaris**
(Climbing Hydrangea)

○ ◐ ●

Strong grower, ideal for a north facing wall. Flat heads of creamy-white flowers smother the plant in June-July.

3 **Jasminum nudiflorum**
(Winter Jasmine)

○ ◐ ●

Vivid yellow flowers appear on naked stems from November-March.

4 **Jasminum officinale**
(Common White Jasmine)

○

Fragrant white flowers borne on slender stems June-September. Vigorous, twining deciduous climber.

5 **Lonicera 'Dropmore Scarlet'**
(Honeysuckle)

○ ◐

Bright scarlet flowers July-September.

6 **Lonicera japonica 'Aureoreticulata'**
(Japanese Honeysuckle)

○ ◐ ● E or Semi E

Neat bright green leaves with a network of gold veins.

7 **Lonicera japonica 'Halliana'**
(Evergreen Honeysuckle)

○ ◐ E or Semi E

Fragrant honeysuckle to twine over an arch or old tree trunk. Flowers June-October.

8 **Lonicera periclymenum 'Belgica'**
(Early Dutch Honeysuckle)

○ ◐

Scented. Flowers May-July.

9 **Lonicera periclymenum 'Serotina'**
(Late Dutch Honeysuckle)

○ ◐

Blooms from July-October. Delightful scent.

○	Full Sun
◐	Semi shade
●	Shade tolerating
E	Evergreen
PP	Prefers pea

All sizes quoted are a general guide but depend upon area, growing conditions and trimming.

WALL/CLIMBING SHRUBS

1 Parthenocissus henryana
○ ◑ ●

Decorative leaf markings. Self-clinging.

2 Parthenocissus quinquefolia
(Virginia Creeper)

Self clinging vine. Brilliant crimson foliage in the Autumn.

3 Parthenocissus tricuspidata 'Veitchii'
(Boston Ivy)(Virginia Creeper)
○ ◑ ●

Vigorous grower. Dramatic fiery autumn colour.

4 Passiflora caerulea
(Passion Flower)
○

Exotic blue and white blooms, freely produced June-September. Protect against winter frosts. Can be grown in large pots or tubs.

5 Polygonum baldschuanicum
(Russian Vine)
○ ◑ ●

Abundance of white flowers during summer and autumn. Unrivalled for quickly covering fences or sheds.

6 Pyracantha
(Firethorn)
○ ◑ ● E

Many varieties available with shades of yellow, red and orange fruits. Attractive flowers early summer.

7 Vitis coignetiae
(Ornamental Vine)
○ ◑ ●

The large handsome leaves turn fiery red in autumn.

8 Vitis 'Brandt'
○ ◑ ●

Attractive autumn foliage and dark purple-black fruits.

9 Wisteria sinensis
○

Racemes of fragrant mauve or deep lilac flowers, May-June.

See Climbing Roses page 60-61 for further selection.

○	Full Sun
◑	Semi shade
●	Shade tolerating
E	Evergreen
PP	Prefers pea

All sizes quoted are a general guide but depend upon area, growing conditions and trimming.

GROUND COVER SHRUBS

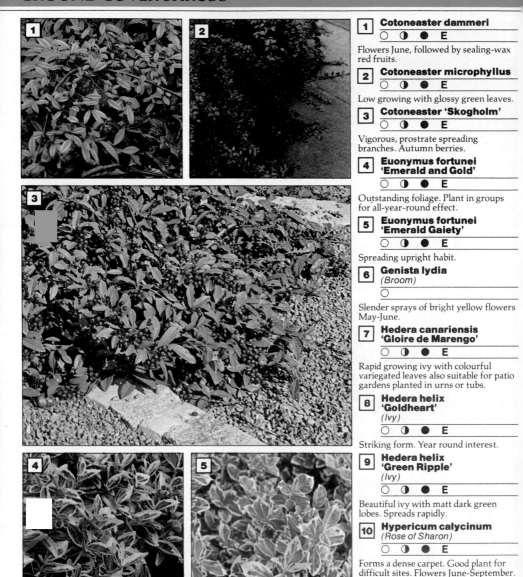

1 Cotoneaster dammeri

○ ◐ ● E

Flowers June, followed by sealing-wax red fruits.

2 Cotoneaster microphyllus

○ ◐ ● E

Low growing with glossy green leaves.

3 Cotoneaster 'Skogholm'

○ ◐ ● E

Vigorous, prostrate spreading branches. Autumn berries.

4 Euonymus fortunei 'Emerald and Gold'

○ ◐ ● E

Outstanding foliage. Plant in groups for all-year-round effect.

5 Euonymus fortunei 'Emerald Gaiety'

○ ◐ ● E

Spreading upright habit.

6 Genista lydia *(Broom)*

○

Slender sprays of bright yellow flowers May-June.

7 Hedera canariensis 'Gloire de Marengo'

○ ◐ ● E

Rapid growing ivy with colourful variegated leaves also suitable for patio gardens planted in urns or tubs.

8 Hedera helix 'Goldheart' *(Ivy)*

○ ◐ ● E

Striking form. Year round interest.

9 Hedera helix 'Green Ripple' *(Ivy)*

○ ◐ ● E

Beautiful ivy with matt dark green lobes. Spreads rapidly.

10 Hypericum calycinum *(Rose of Sharon)*

○ ◐ ● E

Forms a dense carpet. Good plant for difficult sites. Flowers June-September.

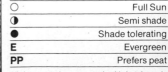

○	Full Sun
◐	Semi shade
●	Shade tolerating
E	Evergreen
PP	Prefers peat

All sizes quoted are a general guide but depend upon area, growing conditions and trimming.

GROUND COVER SHRUBS

1 **Pachysandra terminalis**
● E

Spikes of greenish-white flowers February-March. Useful for carpeting under trees.

2 **Potentilla 'Elizabeth'**
○ ◑ ●

Flowers continuously throughout the Summer.

3 **Viburnum davidii**
○ ◑ ● E

Compact and wide spreading. Flowers June.

4 **Vinca major**
(Greater Periwinkle)
○ ◑ ● E

Forms extensive carpets. Bright blue flowers from April-September.

5 **Vinca major 'Variegata'**
○ ◑ ● E

Vigorous form, brings colour and interest to the garden in winter.

6 **Shrub Rose Candy Rose**
○ ◑

Vigorous spreading habit. Autumn fruit.

7 **Shrub Rose Swany**
○ ◑

Low spreading habit. Flowers June-October.

○	Full Sun
◑	Semi shade
●	Shade tolerating
E	Evergreen
PP	Prefers peat

All sizes quoted are a general guide but depend upon area, growing conditions and trimming.

SMALL SHRUBS: up to 3ft (90cm)

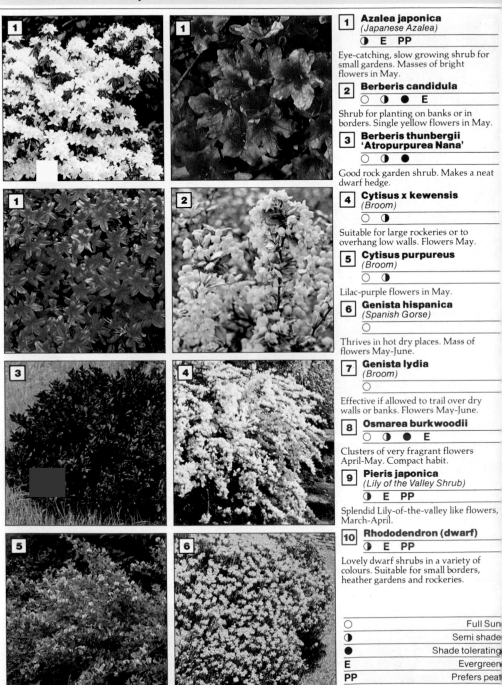

1 Azalea japonica
(Japanese Azalea)

◗ E PP

Eye-catching, slow growing shrub for small gardens. Masses of bright flowers in May.

2 Berberis candidula

○ ◗ ● E

Shrub for planting on banks or in borders. Single yellow flowers in May.

3 Berberis thunbergii 'Atropurpurea Nana'

○ ◗ ●

Good rock garden shrub. Makes a neat dwarf hedge.

4 Cytisus x kewensis
(Broom)

○ ◗

Suitable for large rockeries or to overhang low walls. Flowers May.

5 Cytisus purpureus
(Broom)

○ ◗

Lilac-purple flowers in May.

6 Genista hispanica
(Spanish Gorse)

○

Thrives in hot dry places. Mass of flowers May-June.

7 Genista lydia
(Broom)

○

Effective if allowed to trail over dry walls or banks. Flowers May-June.

8 Osmarea burkwoodii

○ ◗ ● E

Clusters of very fragrant flowers April-May. Compact habit.

9 Pieris japonica
(Lily of the Valley Shrub)

◗ E PP

Splendid Lily-of-the-valley like flowers, March-April.

10 Rhododendron (dwarf)

◗ E PP

Lovely dwarf shrubs in a variety of colours. Suitable for small borders, heather gardens and rockeries.

○	Full Sun
◗	Semi shade
●	Shade tolerating
E	Evergreen
PP	Prefers peat

All sizes quoted are a general guide but depend upon area, growing conditions and trimming.

SPRING FLOWERING

SMALL SHRUBS: **up to 3ft (90cm)**

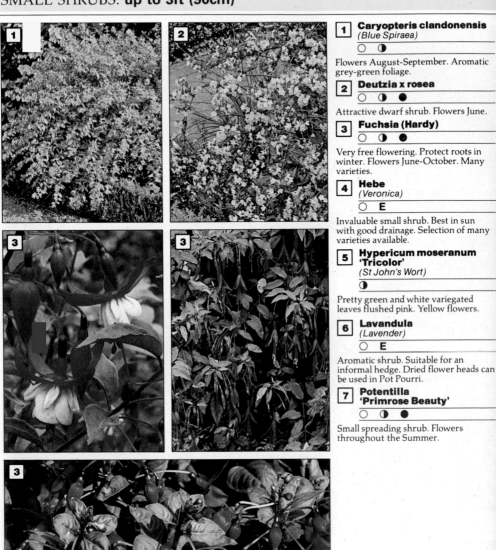

1 **Caryopteris clandonensis**
(Blue Spiraea)

○ ◑

Flowers August-September. Aromatic grey-green foliage.

2 **Deutzia x rosea**

○ ◑ ●

Attractive dwarf shrub. Flowers June.

3 **Fuchsia (Hardy)**

○ ◑ ●

Very free flowering. Protect roots in winter. Flowers June-October. Many varieties.

4 **Hebe**
(Veronica)

○ E

Invaluable small shrub. Best in sun with good drainage. Selection of many varieties available.

5 **Hypericum moseranum 'Tricolor'**
(St John's Wort)

◑

Pretty green and white variegated leaves flushed pink. Yellow flowers.

6 **Lavandula**
(Lavender)

○ E

Aromatic shrub. Suitable for an informal hedge. Dried flower heads can be used in Pot Pourri.

7 **Potentilla 'Primrose Beauty'**

○ ◑ ●

Small spreading shrub. Flowers throughout the Summer.

○	Full Sun
◑	Semi shade
●	Shade tolerating
E	Evergreen
PP	Prefers peat

All sizes quoted are a general guide but depend upon area, growing conditions and trimming.

SUMMER FLOWERING

SMALL SHRUBS: **up to 3ft (90cm)**

1 **Potentilla fruticosa 'Red Ace'**

○ ◑ ●

Glowing red flowers. Flowers June-November.

2 **Potentilla fruticosa 'Tangerine'**

○ ◑ ●

Wide spreading habit. Soft coppery-red flowers in partial shade, becoming bright yellow in full sun. Flowers June-November.

3 **Senecio greyi**

○ E

Forms a dense mound. Bright yellow daisy flowers. Attractive grey foliage.

4 **Spiraea 'Anthony Waterer'**

○ ◑ ●

Flat heads of bright crimson flowers. Excellent low growing plant.

5 **Spiraea 'Little Princess'**

○ ◑ ●

Mound forming habit. Succession of rose-crimson flowers.

○	Full Sun
◑	Semi shade
●	Shade tolerating
E	Evergreen
PP	Prefers peat

All sizes quoted are a general guide but depend upon area, growing conditions and trimming.

SUMMER FLOWERING

SMALL SHRUBS: **up to 3ft (90cm)**

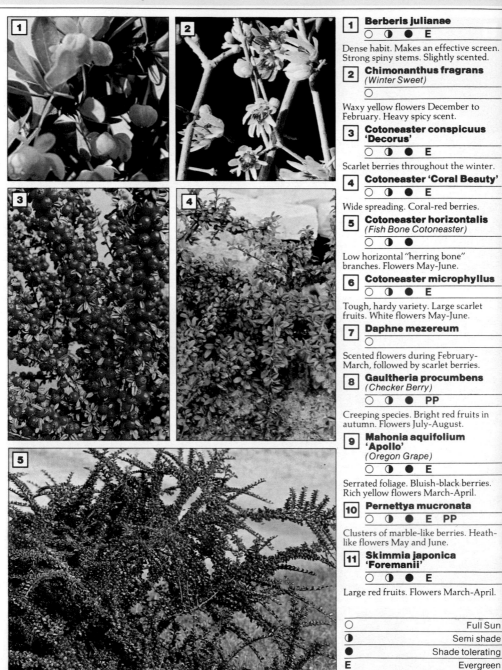

1 Berberis julianae

○ ◑ ● E

Dense habit. Makes an effective screen. Strong spiny stems. Slightly scented.

2 Chimonanthus fragrans
(Winter Sweet)

○

Waxy yellow flowers December to February. Heavy spicy scent.

3 Cotoneaster conspicuus 'Decorus'

○ ◑ ● E

Scarlet berries throughout the winter.

4 Cotoneaster 'Coral Beauty'

○ ◑ ● E

Wide spreading. Coral-red berries.

5 Cotoneaster horizontalis
(Fish Bone Cotoneaster)

○ ◑ ●

Low horizontal "herring bone" branches. Flowers May-June.

6 Cotoneaster microphyllus

○ ◑ ● E

Tough, hardy variety. Large scarlet fruits. White flowers May-June.

7 Daphne mezereum

○

Scented flowers during February-March, followed by scarlet berries.

8 Gaultheria procumbens
(Checker Berry)

○ ◑ ● PP

Creeping species. Bright red fruits in autumn. Flowers July-August.

9 Mahonia aquifolium 'Apollo'
(Oregon Grape)

○ ◑ ● E

Serrated foliage. Bluish-black berries. Rich yellow flowers March-April.

10 Pernettya mucronata

○ ◑ ● E PP

Clusters of marble-like berries. Heath-like flowers May and June.

11 Skimmia japonica 'Foremanii'

○ ◑ ● E

Large red fruits. Flowers March-April.

○	Full Sun
◑	Semi shade
●	Shade tolerating
E	Evergreen
PP	Prefers peat

All sizes quoted are a general guide but depend upon area, growing conditions and trimming.

AUTUMN/WINTER COLOUR

SMALL SHRUBS: **up to 3ft (90cm)**

1 **Acer palmatum 'Dissectum'**
(Japanese Maple)
○ ◑

Slow growing for a sheltered site.

2 **Acer pal. 'Dissectum Atropurpureum'**
(Japanese Maple)
○ ◑

Outstanding. Shelter from cold winds.

3 **Buxus sempervirens**
(Box)
○ ◑ ● E

Ideal for low edging to borders, hedging or topiary.

4 **Hypericum x moseranum 'Tricolor'**
(St. John's Wort)
○

5 **Lonicera nitida 'Baggesen's Gold'**
○ E

Makes a fine hedge.

6 **Pieris 'Forest Flame'**
○ E PP

Stunning combination of white flowers and vivid foliage. Flowers May.

7 **Rosmarinus officinalis 'Jessops Upright'**
○ ◑ E

Blue flowers in May. Aromatic green leaves, undersides white.

8 **Santolina**
(Cotton Lavender)
○ ◑ E

Forms a low growing mound. Woolly silvery leaves. Yellow flowers in July.

9 **Senecio greyi**
○ ◑ E

10 **Spiraea x bumalda 'Goldflame'**
○ ◑ ●

Outstanding young spring growth.

11 **Viburnum davidii**
○ ◑ ● E

Compact habit. White flowers in June.

○	Full Sun
◑	Semi shade
●	Shade tolerating
E	Evergreen
PP	Prefers peat

All sizes quoted are a general guide but depend upon area, growing conditions and trimming.

EVERGREEN/FOLIAGE

MEDIUM SHRUBS: **3ft — 6ft (90 — 180cm)**

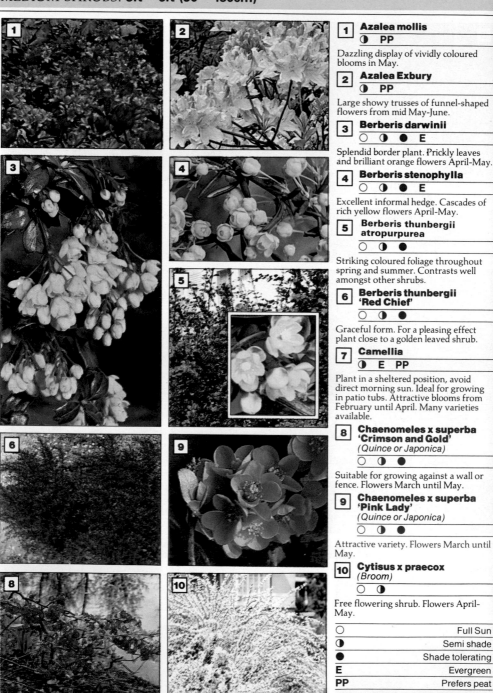

1 Azalea mollis
◐ PP

Dazzling display of vividly coloured blooms in May.

2 Azalea Exbury
◐ PP

Large showy trusses of funnel-shaped flowers from mid May-June.

3 Berberis darwinii
○ ◐ ● E

Splendid border plant. Prickly leaves and brilliant orange flowers April-May.

4 Berberis stenophylla
○ ◐ ● E

Excellent informal hedge. Cascades of rich yellow flowers April-May.

5 Berberis thunbergii atropurpurea
○ ◐ ●

Striking coloured foliage throughout spring and summer. Contrasts well amongst other shrubs.

6 Berberis thunbergii 'Red Chief'
○ ◐ ●

Graceful form. For a pleasing effect plant close to a golden leaved shrub.

7 Camellia
◐ E PP

Plant in a sheltered position, avoid direct morning sun. Ideal for growing in patio tubs. Attractive blooms from February until April. Many varieties available.

8 Chaenomeles x superba 'Crimson and Gold'
(Quince or Japonica)
○ ◐ ●

Suitable for growing against a wall or fence. Flowers March until May.

9 Chaenomeles x superba 'Pink Lady'
(Quince or Japonica)
○ ◐ ●

Attractive variety. Flowers March until May.

10 Cytisus x praecox
(Broom)

Free flowering shrub. Flowers April-May.

○	Full Sun
◐	Semi shade
●	Shade tolerating
E	Evergreen
PP	Prefers peat

All sizes quoted are a general guide but depend upon area, growing conditions and trimming.

SPRING FLOWERING

RHODODENDRONS

Azaleas and Rhododendrons can be advantageously combined to produce a stunning Spring display in any garden.

There are many colours readily available, of which typical selection is shown here.

All Rhododendrons should be planted with plenty of peat. These evergreen plants are happy in semi-shade.

1 **Cunningham's White**

2 **Furnivall's Daughter**

3 **Odee Wright**

4 **Purple Splendour**

5 **Wilgens Ruby**

6 **Bedford**

MEDIUM SHRUBS: **3ft – 6ft (90 – 180cm)**

1 **Cytisus x praecox 'Allgold'**
(Broom)

○ ◑

Attractive arching branches.

2 **Kerria japonica 'Pleniflora'**
(Jew's Mallow)

○ ◑

Abundance of double yellow flowers in April-May.

3 **Magnolia liliiflora 'Nigra'**
(Lily flowered Magnolia)

○ PP

Very choice shrub for attractive display in late Spring.

4 **Magnolia stellata**
(Star Magnolia)

○ ◑ PP

Fragrant flowers March-April.

5 **Prunus cistena**

○ ◑

Rich red leaves. White flowers.

6 **Prunus triloba**

○ ◑

Flowers March-April. Double rosettes of delicate pink flowers.

7 **Spiraea x arguta**
(Bridal Wreath/Foam of May)

○ ◑ ●

Lovely shrub with slender arching stems. Pure white blooms April-May.

8 **Ribes sanguineum**
(Flowering Currant)

○ ◑ ●

Showy bush with pink/red flowers.

9 **Viburnum x burkwoodii**

○ ◑ ● E

Fragrant flowers from January-May.

10 **Viburnum plicatum 'Mariesii'**

○ ◑ ●

Breathtaking shrub. Masses of white florets during May and June.

○	Full Sun
◑	Semi shade
●	Shade tolerating
E	Evergreen
PP	Prefers pea

All sizes quoted are a general guide but depend upon area, growing conditions and trimming.

SPRING FLOWERING

MEDIUM SHRUBS: 3ft – 6ft (90 – 180cm)

1 Choisya ternata
(Mexican Orange Blossom)

○ ◑ ● E

Sweetly scented flowers April-May. Rounded habit. Shelter from cold winds.

2 Cortaderia
(Pampas Grass)

○ ◑ E

For maximum effect, plant Pampas Grass on its own, in a sunny site. Silky plumes in September.

3 Escallonia

○ ◑ ● E

Abundant small flowers June-September.

4 Hibiscus syriacus
(Tree Hollyhock)

○

Sun loving shrub. Large trumpet-shaped blooms are produced in succession from July-October.

5 Hydrangea hortensis
(Mop Head Hydrangea)

○ ◑

Good plant for patio tubs and pots. Keep well watered. Pink, red or blue globular headed flowers July-September.

6 Hydrangea paniculata 'Grandiflora'

○ ◑

Handsome shrub. Panicles of white flowers ageing to pink during August and September.

7 Hypericum 'Hidcote'

○ ◑ Semi E

Delightful border shrub. Large saucer shaped flowers, July-October. Compact habit.

8 Kolkwitzia amabilis
(Beauty Bush)

○ ◑

Graceful drooping branches. Outstanding foxglove-like flowers May-June.

9 Lavatera olba 'Rosea'
(Mallow)

○

Hollyhock-like flowers. Downy grey foliage.

○	Full Sun
◑	Semi shade
●	Shade tolerating
E	Evergreen
PP	Prefers peat

All sizes quoted are a general guide but depend upon area, growing conditions and trimming.

SUMMER FLOWERING

MEDIUM SHRUBS: **3ft – 6ft (90 – 180cm)**

1 **Olearia x haastii**
(Daisy Bush)

○ ◑ E

Versatile shrub. Flowers July-August.

2 **Philadelphus**
(Mock Orange)

Heady fragrance. Attractive blossom June-July. Very adaptable.

3 **Potentilla fruticosa 'Katherine Dykes'**

○ ◑ ●

Excellent plant for the back of a rockery. Abundance of flowers June-September.

4 **Potentilla fruticosa 'Mount Everest'**

○ ◑ ●

White flowers appear from June-September. Easy to grow shrub for a mixed border.

5 **Weigela 'Bristol Ruby'**

○ ◑ ●

A reliable, easy flowering shrub. Strong branches are covered in ruby-red flowers during May and June.

6 **Weigela florida 'Variegata'**

○ ◑ ●

Good border plant. Compact habit. Clear pink flowers and attractive cream-edged leaves. Flowers May-June.

7 **Yucca filamentosa**

○ ◑ E

Long lived shrub. Flowers June-August.

○	Full Sun
◑	Semi shade
●	Shade tolerating
E	Evergreen
PP	Prefers peat

All sizes quoted are a general guide but depend upon area, growing conditions and trimming.

SUMMER FLOWERING

MEDIUM SHRUBS: 3ft – 6ft (90 – 180cm)

1 Cornus
(Dogwoods)

○ ◑ ●

Red or yellow stems. Make an attractive addition to a winter garden. The variety 'Elegantissima' also has interesting variegated foliage in Summer.

2 Corylus avellana 'Contorta'
(Harry Lauder's Walking Stick)

○ ◑ ●

Curiously twisted branches. Showy catkins February.

3 Euonymus alatus

○ ◑ ●

Choice shrub. Glorious autumn colour. Corky winged branches.

4 Hamamelis mollis
(Witch Hazel)

○ ◑ ●

Sweet scented golden yellow flowers are borne on bare twigs December-March. Good autumn leaf colour.

5 Jasminum nudiflorum
(Winter Jasmine)

○ ◑ ●

Superb winter shrub. Flowers November-March. Avoid east facing locations.

6 Mahonia bealei

○ ◑ ● E

Erect racemes of sulphur-yellow flowers December-February. Upright habit.

○	Full Sun
◑	Semi shade
●	Shade tolerating
E	Evergreen
PP	Prefers peat

All sizes quoted are a general guide but depend upon area, growing conditions and trimming.

AUTUMN/WINTER COLOUR

MEDIUM SHRUBS: 3ft – 6ft (90 – 180cm)

1 | **Mahonia 'Charity'**

○ ◐ ● **E**

Excellent evergreen shrub. Ascending racemes of exquisitely scented flowers from December to February.

2 | **Mahonia japonica**

○ ◐ ● **E**

Choice shrub with magnificent pinnate leaves. Flowers January-March. Not as tall as Charity or bealii.

3 | **Mahonia pinnata**

○ ◐ ● **E**

Spiny dense shrub. Sea-green foliage. Flowers March-April.

4 | **Symphoricarpos Chenaultii x Hancock**

○ ◐ ●

Glistening pink berries from October-February.

5 | **Viburnum x bodnantense 'Dawn'**

○ ◐ ●

Densely packed clusters of rich pink and white fragrant flowers during late autumn and winter.

6 | **Viburnum tinus**

○ ◐ ● **E**

Can be planted as an informal hedge or screen. Flattened heads of flowers November to May. Dark glossy foliage.

○	Full Sun
◐	Semi shade
●	Shade tolerating
E	Evergreen
PP	Prefers peat

All sizes quoted are a general guide but depend upon area, growing conditions and trimming.

AUTUMN/WINTER COLOUR

MEDIUM SHRUBS: **3ft – 6ft (90 – 180cm)**

1 **Acer palmatum 'Atropurpureum'**
(Japanese Maple)

○ ◑ ●

Outstanding autumn colour.

2 **Berberis 'Parkjuweel'**

○ ◑ Semi E

Dense prickly habit. Leaves colour in Autumn. Yellow flowers in Spring.

3 **Berberis thunbergii 'Rose Glow'**

○ ◑ ●

Distinctive mottling on young foliage.

4 **Cornus alba 'Elegantissima'**
(Variegated Dogwood)

○ ◑ ●

Pretty foliage and red winter stems.

5 **Corylus maxima 'Purpurea'**
(Purple Leaf Filbert)

○ ◑ ●

Tolerates bleak sites. Catkins February.

6 **Stranvaesia Davidiana**

○ ◑ ● E

7 **Cotinus coggyria 'Royal Purple'**
(Purple Smoke Bush)

○ ◑

8 **Elaeagnus pungens 'Maculata'**
(Oleaster)

○ ◑ ● E

9 **Weigela Variegata**

○ ◑ ● E

10 **Photinia x fraseri 'Red Robin'**

○ ◑ ● E

Brilliant red young leaves in Spring.

11 **Prunus laurocerasus 'Otto Luyken'**

○ ◑ ● E

12 **Sambucus racemosa 'Plumosa Aurea'**
(Golden Cut Leaf Elder)

○ ◑ ●

○	Full Sun
◑	Semi shade
●	Shade tolerating
E	Evergreen
PP	Prefers peat

All sizes quoted are a general guide but depend upon area, growing conditions and trimming.

EVERGREEN/FOLIAGE

LARGE SHRUBS: **over 6ft (180cm)**

1 Amelanchier
(Snowy Mespilus)

○　◑　●

Grows well in most situations. Cloud of white flowers in April. Leaves richly coloured in Autumn.

2 Berberis x ottawensis 'Superba'

○　◑

Attractive purple foliage. Quick growing variety. Yellow flowers.

3 Ceanothus dentatus

○　E

Bright blue flowers May and June.

4 Forsythia

○　◑　●

Long branches laden with bell-like flowers March-April.

5 Magnolia x soulangiana
(Tulip Flowered Magnolia)

○　PP

Spectactular variety. Magnificent tulip shaped blooms appear April-early May. Prefers shelter from early morning sun.

6 Rhododendron ponticum
(Wild Rhododendron)

◑　E　PP

Funnel-shaped flowers from May to June. Useful species for forming a large hedge or windbreak.

○	Full Sun
◑	Semi shade
●	Shade tolerating
E	Evergreen
PP	Prefers peat

All sizes quoted are a general guide but depend upon area, growing conditions and trimming.

LARGE SHRUBS: **over 6ft (180cm)**

1 Buddleia alternifolia
○

Arching branches. Fragrant lilac flowers are produced in June. Forms a large shrub or tree.

2 Buddleia davidii
(Butterfly Bush)
○

Strong grower. Responds to hard pruning in March. Fragrant spikes, attractive to Butterflies. Flowers July-September.

3 Ceanothus 'Gloire de Versailles'
○

Requires a warm site in full sun. Large loose clusters of powder-blue flowers June-October.

4 Pyracantha
(Firethorn)
○ ◑ ● E

Handsome berrying shrub. Effective planted against a wall or in a mixed border. Attractive white flowers.

5 Syringa
(Lilac)
○ ◑ ●

Fragrant double or single blooms. Lilacs are happy in most soils, especially good on chalk. Flowers May-June.

6 Viburnum opulus 'Sterile'
(Snowball Bush)
○ ◑ ●

Very decorative. Round heads of sterile flowers May and June.

○	Full Sun
◑	Semi shade
●	Shade tolerating
E	Evergreen
PP	Prefers peat

All sizes quoted are a general guide but depend upon area, growing conditions and trimming.

SUMMER FLOWERING

1 **Amelanchier**
(*Snowy Mespilus*)

○ ◑ ●

Leaves richly coloured. White flowers
in Spring.

2 **Arbutus**
(*Strawberry Tree*)

○ ◑ ● E

Large picturesque shrub for a warm
corner. Strawberry like fruits. Flowers
produced late autumn.

3 **Cotoneaster 'Cornubia'**

○ ◑ ● Semi E

Excellent screening shrub. Long
branches are weighed down by
bunches of profuse red fruits.

4 **Cotoneaster franchetii**

○ ◑ ● Semi E

Graceful arching form. Ovoid orange
red berries. Good for hedging.

5 **Pyracantha**
(*Firethorn*)

○ ◑ ● E

Thorny evergreen. Sumptuous
clusters of bright berries last from
September until March. White flowers
in Summer.

6 **Rhus typhina**
(*Sumach*)

○ ◑ ●

Good natured species. Easily
cultivated. Striking foliage with
intense autumn colour.

7 **Parrotia persica**

○ ◑ ●

Rich autumn tints of amber, crimson
and gold. Slow growing.

○	Full Sun
◑	Semi shade
●	Shade tolerating
E	Evergreen
PP	Prefers pea

*All sizes quoted are a general guide but depend
upon area, growing conditions and trimming.*

LARGE SHRUBS: **over 6ft (180cm)**

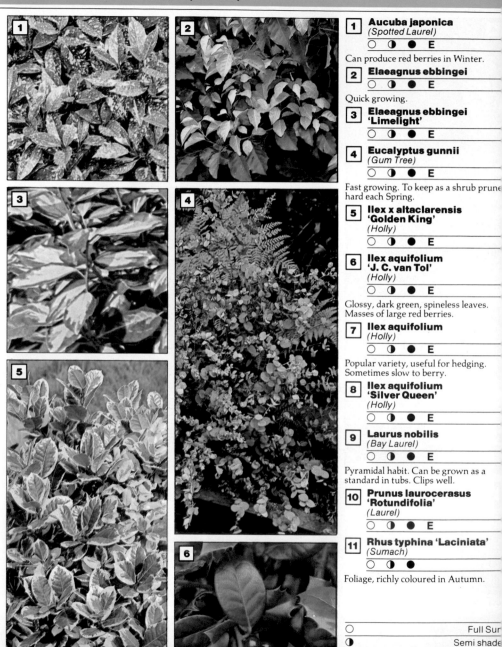

1 **Aucuba japonica**
(Spotted Laurel)

○ ◑ ● E

Can produce red berries in Winter.

2 **Elaeagnus ebbingei**

○ ◑ ● E

Quick growing.

3 **Elaeagnus ebbingei 'Limelight'**

○ ◑ ● E

4 **Eucalyptus gunnii**
(Gum Tree)

○ ◑ ● E

Fast growing. To keep as a shrub prune hard each Spring.

5 **Ilex x altaclarensis 'Golden King'**
(Holly)

○ ◑ ● E

6 **Ilex aquifolium 'J. C. van Tol'**
(Holly)

○ ◑ ● E

Glossy, dark green, spineless leaves. Masses of large red berries.

7 **Ilex aquifolium**
(Holly)

○ ◑ ● E

Popular variety, useful for hedging. Sometimes slow to berry.

8 **Ilex aquifolium 'Silver Queen'**
(Holly)

○ ◑ ● E

9 **Laurus nobilis**
(Bay Laurel)

○ ◑ ● E

Pyramidal habit. Can be grown as a standard in tubs. Clips well.

10 **Prunus laurocerasus 'Rotundifolia'**
(Laurel)

○ ◑ ● E

11 **Rhus typhina 'Laciniata'**
(Sumach)

○ ◑ ●

Foliage, richly coloured in Autumn.

○	Full Sun
◑	Semi shade
●	Shade tolerating
E	Evergreen
PP	Prefers pea

All sizes quoted are a general guide but depend upon area, growing conditions and trimming.

TREES

FLOWERING/BERRYING TREES

1 **Cotoneaster 'Cornubia'**
♠

Cream flowers appear in July. Profuse red berries weigh down the branches in Autumn.

2 **Crataegus oxyacantha 'Pauls Scarlet'**
♠

Tough hardy tree with double-scarlet blooms. Very reliable.

3 **Laburnum watereri x 'Vossii'**
(Golden Rain Tree)
♠

Free flowering hybrid which produces little seed. Chains of yellow pea-like flowers May-June. N.B. Laburnum seeds are highly poisonous.

4 **Malus floribunda**
(Japanese Crab)
♠

Densely branched. Flowers April-May. Autumn fruits.

5 **Malus 'Golden Hornet'**
(Ornamental Crab)
♠

Bright yellow conical fruits. Flowers May.

6 **Malus 'John Downie'**
(Ornamental Crab)
♠

White flowers in May. Bright orange and red fruits. May be used in preserves.

♠	Spreading
▲	Conical
▮	Columnar
♣	Weeping

FLOWERING/BERRYING TREES

1 Malus 'Profusion'
(Flowering Crab)
♠

Excellent choice for the smaller garden. Wine-red slightly fragrant flowers appear in April.

2 Malus 'Royalty'
♠

Deep purple foliage with large crimson flowers.

3 Prunus 'Amanogawa'
(Lombardy Poplar Cherry)
♦

Narrow habit. Shell pink flowers April-May. Ideal for a small garden.

4 Prunus avium 'Plena'
(Double Gean)
♣

Pendant clusters of double white flowers April-May. Splendid specimen.

5 Prunus 'Kanzan'
(Flowering Cherry)

Stiffly ascending branches are smothered with double purple-pink blossoms April-May.

6 Prunus 'Kiku-shidare Sakura'
(Cheals Weeping)
♠

Pendulous branches wreathed with double deep pink florets during April.

7 Prunus subhirtella 'Autumnalis'
(Autumn Cherry)
♠

Semi-double white flowers November-March.

8 Prunus triloba
(Flowering Almond)

Double rosette-like flowers.

9 Sorbus aucuparia
(Rowan/Mountain Ash)
♠

Alternative native tree. Heavy bunches of bright orange-red berries start to ripen in August.

♠	Spreading
♦	Conical
♦	Columnar
♠	Weeping

FOLIAGE TREES

1. **Acer negundo 'Aureomarginatum'**

2. **Acer platanoides 'Crimson King'**
   (Purple-Leaf Maple)

3. **Acer platanoides 'Drummondii'**
   (Variegated Maple)

4. **Acer pseudoplatanus 'Brilliantissimum'**
   (Pink-Leaf Maple)

5. **Acer 'Simon-Louis Freres'**
   (Variegated Maple)

6. **Betula pendula**
   (Silver Birch)

7. **Fagus sylvatica purpurea**
   (Purple Beech)

8. **Liquidambar**
   (Sweet Gum)

9. **Populus x candicans 'Aurora'**
   (Variegated Poplar)

10. **Prunus cerasifera 'Nigra'**
    (Purple Leaf Plum)

11. **Robinia pseudoacacia 'Frisia'**
    (False Acacia)

12. **Salix matsudana 'Tortuosa'**
    (Contorted Willow)

13. **Sorbus aria 'Lutescens'**
    (Whitebeam)

14. **Sorbus 'Embley'**
    (discolor)

Spreading
Conical

53

WEEPING TREES

1 **Laburnum alpinum**
(Weeping Laburnum)

A weeping form of this familiar tree.

2 **Pyrus salicifolia 'Pendula'**
(Weeping Willow-Leaf Pear)

Graceful small tree creates an unusual colour effect. Silvery willow-like leaves.

3 **Malus 'Red Jade'**

Alternative weeping tree, covered in pink and white flowers.

4 **Salix x chrysocoma**
(Golden Weeping Willow)

Spectacular weeping tree. Wide spreading. Strongly arching branches. Slender bright green leaves. Prefers moist soil.

5 **Salix caprea 'Pendula'**
(Kilmarnock Willow)

Huge yellow spring catkins on stiffly pendulous branches.

6 **Caragana Arborescens 'Pendula'**

Small weeping tree with delicate foliage and yellow flowers in Spring.

7 **Fagus sylvatica 'Purpurea Pendula'**

The weeping purple beech with dark purple leaves.

8 **Prunus 'Kiku-shidare Sakura'**
(Cheals Weeping)

Deep pink flowers clothe the drooping branches March-April. Very attractive.

	Spreading
	Conica
	Columna
	Weeping

HEDGING

1 **Berberis thunbergii atropurpurea**
H: 5ft (150cm) PD: 2ft (60cm)

2 **Berberis x stenophylla**
E H: 5ft (150cm) PD: 2ft (60cm)
Yellow flowers April-May.

3 **Cupressocyparis leylandii** *(Leyland Cypress)*
E H: 12ft + (360cm)
PD: 2½ft (75cm)
Fast growing. Golden forms available.

4 **Crataegus monogya** *(Hawthorn or Quickthorn)*
H: 5ft + (150cm) PD: 1ft (30cm)

5 **Fagus purpurea** *(Purple Beech or Copper Beech)*
H: 5ft + (150cm) PD: 1½ft (45cm)

6 **Lavandula** *(Lavender)*
H: 2ft (60cm) PD: 1½ft (45cm)

7 **Ligustrum ovalifolium** *(Privet)*
Semi E H: 4-5ft (120-150cm)
PD: 1ft (30cm)

8 **Ligustrum ovalifolium 'Aureum'** *(Golden Privet)*
Semi E H: 4-5ft (120-150cm)
PD: 1ft (30cm)

9 **Lonicera nitida**
E H: 4ft (120cm) PD: 1ft (30cm)

10 **Buxus sempervirens** *(Box)*
E H: 1½-3ft (45-90cm)
PD: 6" (15cm)

11 **Prunus laurocerasus** *(Laurel)*
E H: 5ft (150cm) PD: 2ft (60cm)

12 **Pyracantha** *(Firethorn)*
E H: 4ft (120cm) PD: 2ft (60cm)
Orange-red berries in the Autumn.

13 **Rosa rugosa**
H: 4-5ft (120-150cm)
PD: 3ft (90cm)

14 **Thuja plicata** *(Western Red Cedar)*
E H: 10ft + (300cm)
PD: 2ft (60cm)

E	Evergreen
H	Height
PD	Planting Distance

*All heights and planting distances quoted are a
general guide but depend upon area, growing
conditions and trimming.*

ROSES

Beautiful shaped blooms borne on long stems. Excellent for cutting and in formal displays.

1	**Apricot Silk**	SF
2	**Blue Moon**	VF
3	**Chicago Peace**	SF
4	**Ernest H Morse**	VF
5	**Fragrant Cloud**	VF
6	**Grandpa Dickson**	SF
7	**Mischief**	SF
8	**Pascali**	SF
9	**Piccadilly**	SF
10	**Silver Jubilee**	SF
11	**Super Star**	F
12	**Whisky Mac**	VF

This is a small selection of the many varieties and colours available.

F	Fragrant
VF	Very Fragrant
SF	Slightly Fragrant

LARGE FLOWERED/HYBRID TEA ROSES

CLUSTER FLOWERED/FLORIBUNDA ROSES

Unrivalled for providing a colourful, reliable and long-lasting display throughout the summer. For maximum effect plant in massed groups.

1	**Allgold**
	SF

2	**Chinatown**
	F

3	**City of Leeds**
	SF

4	**Elizabeth of Glamis**
	F

5	**Evelyn Fison**
	SF

6	**Glenfiddich**
	SF

7	**Iceberg**
	SF

8	**Orange Sensation**
	F

9	**Paddy McGredy**
	SF

10	**Queen Elizabeth**
	SF

11	**Tip Top**
	SF

12	**Topsi**

This is a small selection of the many varieties and colours available.

F	Fragrant
VF	Very Fragrant
SF	Slightly Fragrant

CLIMBING/RAMBLING ROSES

CLIMBING

Will provide colour and cover on walls, trellis, arches and fences. Most have large hybrid tea type blooms.

1 **Compassion**
VF

2 **Danse du Feu**

3 **Golden Showers**
F

4 **Handel**
SF

5 **Mermaid**
F

6 **Paul's Scarlet**
SF

7 **Pink Perpetue**
SF

8 **Schoolgirl**
F

9 **Swan Lake**
SF

10 **Zepherine Drouhin**
VF

RAMBLING

Charming roses for pillars, pergolas, fences or sloping banks.

11 **Albertine**
VF

12 **Dorothy Perkins**

13 **Emily Gray**
F

14 **Excelsa**

15 **New Dawn**
F

This is a small selection of the many varieties and colours available.

F	Fragrant
VF	Very Fragrant
SF	Slightly Fragrant

OLD FASHIONED SHRUB ROSES

May be planted in groups, singly, in borders or as hedges.

1	**Roseraie de L'Hay**	
	F	
2	**Frühlingsgold**	
	F	
3	**Fred Loads**	
	F	
4	**Marjorie Fair**	
	F	
5	**Nevada**	
	SF	
6	**Canary Bird**	
	F	
7	**Ballerina**	
	SF	
8	**Marguerite Hilling**	
	SF	
9	**Rose d'Amour**	
	F	

F	Fragrant
VF	Very Fragrant
SF	Slightly Fragrant

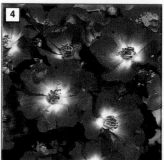

STANDARD ROSES

Ideal as specimens or to border paths and driveways. Upright and weeping varieties are available in many colours.

It is advisable to stake and tie well, to avoid stem damage.

LOW GROWING/SPREADING CONIFERS

1 Juniperus communis 'Depressa Aurea'
✕ *(Golden Canadian Juniper)*
Young foliage golden-yellow.

2 Juniperus communis 'Repanda'
✕ Deservately popular variety.

3 Juniperus horizontalis 'Glauca'
✕ Slender sprays of steel blue foliage.

4 Juniperus x media 'Old Gold'
✳ Bronze-gold foliage. Compact habit.

5 Juniperus procumbens 'Nana'
✕ Makes a dense mat. Seen to advantage growing over a wall.

6 Juniperus sabina 'Tamariscifolia'
✕ *(Spanish Juniper)*
Popular wide-spreading conifer. Suitable for a bank or wall.

7 Juniperus squamata 'Blue Carpet'
✕ Low growing carpet of intense silver-blue.

8 Juniperus squamata 'Blue Star'
✳ Dense silver-blue foliage year round.

9 Picea abies 'Nidiformis'
(Bird's Nest Spruce)
✳ Particularly attractive in summer when foliage tips become bright green.

10 Picea pungens prostrata
Superb form.
✳

11 Pinus mugo pumilio
(Dwarf Mountain Pine)
✳ Very attractive dwarf pine with distinctive winter buds.

12 Picea strobus 'Nana'
(Dwarf Weymouth Pine)
✳ Delightful plant with dense glaucous needles.

Symbol	Meaning
✕	Prostrate
✳	Semi Prostrate
●	Bush
▲	Conical
♦	Columnar
♦	Broadly Columnar
좀	Pendulous

All plants are evergreen and will grow in sun or shade. Conifers prefer peaty soil.

MINIATURE CONIFERS

1 **Chamaecyparis lawsoniana 'Forsteckensis'**
Grey-green foliage.

2 **Chamaecyparis lawsoniana 'Minima Aurea'**
Conical shaped with bright yellow foliage.

3 **Chamaecyparis lawsoniana 'Minima Glauca'**
Globular bush with densely packed sea-green foliage.

4 **Chamaecyparis obtusa 'Nana Lutea'**
Dense sprays of golden-yellow foliage.

5 **Chamaecyparis lawsoniana 'Pygmaea Argentea'**
Bluish green foliage, tipped creamy-white.

6 **Chamaecyparis pisifera 'Nana'**
Lovely dome shaped bush. Tight, closely packed dark green foliage.

7 **Chamaecyparis pisifera 'Plumosa Rogersii'**
Benefits from a sheltered position. Bright golden-yellow during Summer.

8 **Juniperus communis 'Compressa'**
Ideal for the rock garden. Cone shaped and very dense. Effective planted in groups.

9 **Picea abies 'Echiniformis'**
Bluish-grey green foliage, densely packed.

10 **Picea abies 'Ohlendorffii'**
Light green summer foliage.

11 **Picea pungens 'Globosa'**
Dense habit. Silver-blue foliage.

12 **Thuja occidentalis 'Globosa'**
Globular habit.

✕	Prostrate
✳	Semi Prostrate
🟤	Bush
▲	Conical
▮	Columnar
▮	Broadly Columnar
🌲	Pendulous

All plants are evergreen and will grow in sun or shade. Conifers prefer peaty soil. All sizes quoted are a general guide but depend upon area, growing conditions and trimming.

Up to 18ins (45cms) at 10 years

DWARF CONIFERS

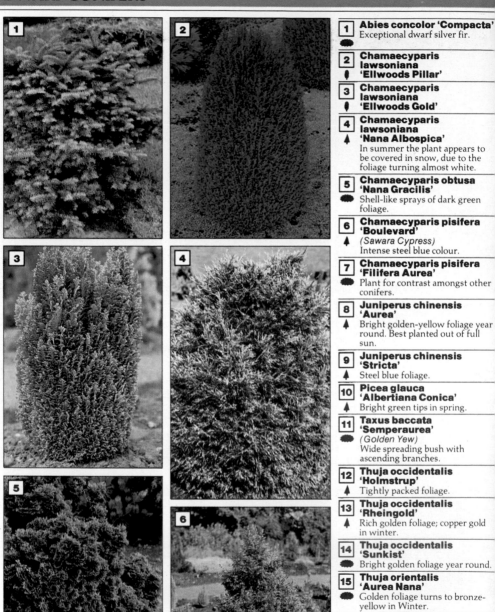

1 Abies concolor 'Compacta'
Exceptional dwarf silver fir.

2 Chamaecyparis lawsoniana 'Ellwoods Pillar'

3 Chamaecyparis lawsoniana 'Ellwoods Gold'

4 Chamaecyparis lawsoniana 'Nana Albospica'
In summer the plant appears to be covered in snow, due to the foliage turning almost white.

5 Chamaecyparis obtusa 'Nana Gracilis'
Shell-like sprays of dark green foliage.

6 Chamaecyparis pisifera 'Boulevard'
(Sawara Cypress)
Intense steel blue colour.

7 Chamaecyparis pisifera 'Filifera Aurea'
Plant for contrast amongst other conifers.

8 Juniperus chinensis 'Aurea'
Bright golden-yellow foliage year round. Best planted out of full sun.

9 Juniperus chinensis 'Stricta'
Steel blue foliage.

10 Picea glauca 'Albertiana Conica'
Bright green tips in spring.

11 Taxus baccata 'Semperaurea'
(Golden Yew)
Wide spreading bush with ascending branches.

12 Thuja occidentalis 'Holmstrup'
Tightly packed foliage.

13 Thuja occidentalis 'Rheingold'
Rich golden foliage; copper gold in winter.

14 Thuja occidentalis 'Sunkist'
Bright golden foliage year round.

15 Thuja orientalis 'Aurea Nana'
Golden foliage turns to bronze-yellow in Winter.

Bush
Conical
Columnar

All plants are evergreen and will grow in sun or shade. Conifers prefer peaty soil. All sizes quoted are a general guide but depend upon area, growing conditions and trimming.

18ins (45cm) up to 3ft (1m) at 10 years

MEDIUM CONIFERS

1 Chamaecyparis lawsoniana 'Allumii'
Beautiful conical shape. Flattened sprays of soft blue-grey foliage.

2 Chamaecyparis lawsoniana 'Backhousiana'
Contrasts well with golden and blue varieties.

3 Chamaecyparis lawsoniana 'Columnaris Glauca'
Ideal as specimen tree to provide a focal point in the garden. Bluish-grey foliage.

4 Chamaecyparis lawsoniana 'Ellwoodii'
Popular.

5 Chamaecyparis lawsoniana 'Erecta Viridis'
Vivid green foliage year round.

6 Chamaecyparis lawsoniana 'Fletcheri'
Splendid conifer with broad columnar habit. Grey-green foliage, bronze tinged in winter.

7 Chamaecyparis lawsoniana 'Lanei'
For best effect plant against a dark background.

8 Chamaecyparis lawsoniana 'Pottenii'
Light green foliage in soft feathery sprays.

9 Chamaecyparis lawsoniana 'Stardust'
Yellow, bronze tipped foliage. Narrow habit.

10 Chamaecyparis lawsoniana 'Lutea'
A graceful conifer which retains good winter colour.

✕	Prostrate
✱	Semi Prostrate
🌳	Bush
▲	Conical
●	Columnar
●	Broadly Columnar
🌲	Pendulous

All plants are evergreen and will grow in sun or shade. Conifers prefer peaty soil. All sizes quoted are a general guide but depend upon area, growing conditions and trimming.

3ft (1m) up to 9ft (3m) at 10 years

MEDIUM CONIFERS

1 Chamaecyparis nootkatensis 'Pendula'
⋔ Graceful pendulous branches.

2 Chamaecyparis pisifera 'Plumosa Aurea'
▲ Plant in a sunny position. Dislikes clay. Looks well planted amongst heathers.

3 Juniperus x media 'Pfitzeriana'
✕ *(Pfitzer Juniper)*
Ascending branches with drooping tips.

4 Juniperus x media 'Pfitzeriana Aurea'
✕ Irregular graceful habit.

5 Juniperus communis 'Hibernica'
♦ *(Irish Juniper)*
Excellent conifer. Narrow columnar habit.

6 Juniperus scopulorum 'Skyrocket'
♦ Fast growing variety with glaucous foliage. "Pencil-like" form.

7 Picea orientalis 'Aurea'
▲ Especially attractive in spring when it is covered in golden tips.

8 Picea pungens 'Koster'
▲ *(Kosters Blue Spruce)*
Keeps its colour well through the winter. Leaves silvery-blue.

9 Taxus baccata 'Fastigiata'
♦ *(Irish Yew)*
Fine specimen tree. Black-green leaves. Erect habit.

10 Taxus baccata 'Fastigiata Aureo-marginata'
♦ *(Golden Irish Yew)*
Striking winter colour. Plant in a sunny position.

11 Thuja occidentalis 'Smargd'
▲ Good for hedging. Neat pyramidal habit.

✕	Prostrate
✕	Semi Prostrate
●	Bush
▲	Conical
♦	Columnar
♦	Broadly Columnar
⋔	Pendulous

All plants are evergreen and will grow in sun or shade. Conifers prefer peaty soil. All sizes quoted are a general guide but depend upon area, growing conditions and trimming.

8ft (1m) up to 9ft (3m) at 10 years

LARGE CONIFERS

1 Abies concolor
(Colorado White Fir)
Impressive tall growing conifer with large cones.

2 Abies nordmanniana
(Caucasian Fir)
Tiered horizontal branches. Glossy green leaves, banded white underneath.

3 Cedrus atlantica glauca
(Blue Cedar)
Imposing tree with handsome blue foliage. Outstanding form.

4 Cedrus deodara
(Deodar Cedar)
A fine specimen tree. Blue-grey foliage on young trees.

5 Cupressocyparis leylandii
(Leyland Cypress)
Fast growing conifer of dense habit. Excellent for hedge or screen.

6 Cupressocyparis leylandii 'Castlewellan Gold'
(Golden Leyland Cypress)
Very adaptable form makes an attractive hedge. Golden foliage year round, brighter in summer.

7 Metasequoia glyptostroboides
Foliage bright green in early Summer, becoming bronze, then golden in late Summer.

8 Picea omorika
(Serbian Spruce)
Short drooping branches with an upward curve at the tips. Slender habit.

9 Thuja plicata
(Western Red Cedar)
Ideal for hedge or screen. Stands severe cutting. Deep lustrous green leaves.

✕	Prostrate
✻	Semi Prostrate
●	Bush
▲	Conical
♦	Columnar
●	Broadly Columnar
☘	Pendulous

All plants are evergreen and will grow in sun or shade. Conifers prefer peaty soil. All sizes quoted are a general guide but depend upon area, growing conditions and trimming.

Over 9ft (3m) at 10 years

ALPINE/ROCKERY PLANTS

1 Alyssum saxatile

Fine display of bright showy flowers. Suitable for rockeries or growing over walls. Flowers April-June.

2 Arabis

Reliable plant with charming pink or white flowers, for front of a border or on walls. Flowers April-May.

3 Arenaria

Deep green foliage smothered in white flowers in Summer.

4 Aubrieta

Cascades of lilac, pink, purple or red flowers. Excellent for rockeries, banks and walls. After flowering trim back with shears.

5 Campanula carpatica

Dainty cup shaped blooms produced June-August. Blue and white varieties available.

6 Dianthus alpinus

Mat forming variety studded with large pink flowers May-July.

7 Geranium subcaulescens

Long-living plants with a long flowering period.

8 Helianthemum
(Rock Rose)

Long-flowering plant. Indispendable for the rock garden. Available in a wide range of colours. Trim after flowering.

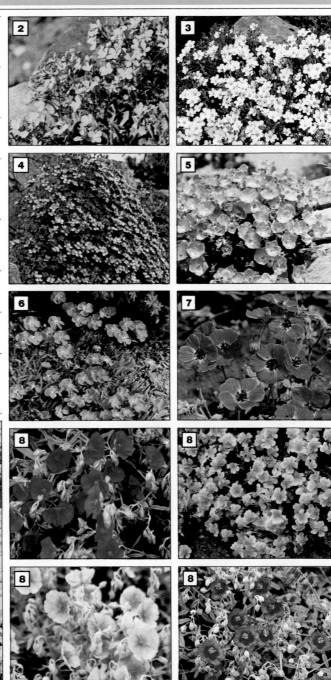

Most alpine/rockery plants thrive better when planted in a sunny position.

ALPINE/ROCKERY PLANTS

1 Hypericum polyphyllum

Bright yellow flowers produced on low studded mounds. Good for raised beds, walls or rockeries.

2 Iberis sempervirens
(Rock Candytuft)

Vigorous, easy plant. Excellent for dry walls. Wide heads of snow white flowers April-June.

3 Lithospermum diffusum 'Heavenly Blue'

Beautiful prostrate plant. Bright sky-blue flowers. Suitable for large troughs or rockeries.

4 Lychnis alpina

Sun loving plant. Pale purple flower heads. Compact leafy tufts.

5 Armeria maritima
(Sea Pink Thrift)

Grey-green hummocks with drum-stick flowers borne on slender stems from May-August. Attractive plant.

6 Aster alpinus

Neat clumps of daisy-like flowers May-June.

7 Campanula muralis

Clumpy growth, flowers June-September.

8 Dianthus caesius
(Cheddar Pink)

Blue-grey foliage. Flowers May-July.

9 Dianthus deltoides

Forms a brilliant carpet of small red flowers June-August.

10 Gentiana acaulis

Exquisite blue trumpet-like flowers May-June.

11 Leontopodium
(Edelweiss)

Fascinating flowers June-August. Suitable for troughs.

12 Sempervivum
(House Leek)

Form rosettes which expand as others begin to grow from underneath. Flower in early summer.

13 Mimulus

Lipped, trumpet-shaped flowers in some brilliant colours. Flowers June-July.

Most alpine/rockery plants thrive better when planted in a sunny position.

ALPINE/ROCKERY PLANTS

1 Oxalis adenophylla

Tufts of crumply grey leaves and larger funnel shaped flowers in late Spring.

2 Phlox subulata

Many varieties and bright colours available. Good carpeters. Flower in Spring and early Summer.

3 Primula rosea

Flower clusters in early Spring. Easy to grow.

4 Saponaria ocymoides *(Soapwort)*

Pretty trailing plants, ideal for wall, or crevices. Bright pink flowers May-August.

5 Saxifraga *(mossy)*

Tufted rosettes of fresh green foliage. Perfect for rockeries. Prefers light shade.

6 Sedum acre *(Stonecrop)*

Tough, low growing plant with vigorous habit. Good for dry stone walls and hot sunny banks.

7 Sedum 'Ruby Glow'

Rich rose-crimson flower heads. Excellent plant for front of border or a raised bed. Flowers July-August.

8 Sedum spathulifolium

Form powdery grey-purple mounds. Yellow flowers June-July.

9 Sedum spurium

Dense flattened heads of vivid pink flowers appear July-August. Good ground cover plant.

10 Silene schafta

Invaluable rockery plant, with neat green leaves and bright pink flowers June-October.

11 Thymus serpyllum *(Thyme)*

Creeping plant, forms an aromatic mat for paved areas or herb garden.

12 Veronica gentianoides

Handsome pale blue flowers borne in May and June. Suitable for the front of a border.

13 Viola cornuta

Long succession of pansy-like flowers May-August.

Most alpine/rockery plants thrive better when planted in a sunny position.

HEATHERS

1 Winter flowering heathers

2 Summer flowering heathers

3 Foliage heathers

Heathers are evergreen, easy-to-grow and produce good ground cover. They prefer an open, sunny position where they can enjoy plenty of light and fresh air. For best results use plenty of peat when planting.

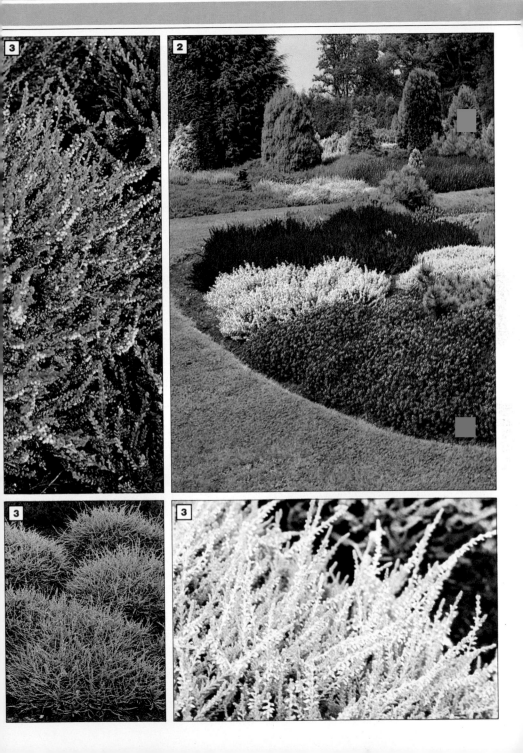

HERBS

1 Sweet Basil
Ocimum basilicum

H x S: 2 x 1ft (60 x 30cm)

Essential ingredient for many pasta dishes. Chopped leaves add flavour to soups, salads and fish dishes. Pick leaves before plant flowers. Purple tinged flowers.

2 Sweet Bay
Laurus nobilis

H x S: Up to 30 x 20ft (900 x 600cm)

Dried leaves can be used to flavour stews, soups and rice. Essential ingredient of bouquet garni. Can be grown as a standard in tubs.

3 Chives
Allium schoenoprasum

H x S: 8 x 10in (20 x 25cm)

Perennial, suitable for small pots and tubs. Use mild onion flavoured leaves, chopped, in egg and cheese dishes. Pretty purple pin-cushion like flowers should be removed if the plant is grown for culinary purposes.

4 Dill
Peucedanum graveolens

H x S: 3 x 1ft (90 x 30cm)

Pungent annual herb. Excellent with cucumber and fish dishes. Seeds can be used in pickles. Dill tea is said to aid sufferers of insomnia. Pick leaves as needed.

5 Fennel
Foeniculum vulgare

H x S: 5 x 2ft (150 x 60cm)

Small yellow flowers and feathery foliage. Cook young leaves with fish or veal. Pungent seeds are good in sauces. Thick stems may be braised like celery.

6 Feverfew
Chrysanthemum
parthenium

H x S: 1 x 1ft (30 x 30cm)

Small daisy flowers and strong scented foliage. It is said that a 3 inch leaf per day help sufferers of migraine and the leaves help to soothe insect bites.

H x S: Height x Spread

Most herbs prefer to be in a sunny position but the majority will thrive in any position.

1 Lavender
Lavandula officinalis

H x S: 3 x 2ft (90 x 60cm)

The strongly scented flowers can be dried and used for pot pourri.

2 Marjoram
Origanum

H x S: 2 x 1ft (60 x 30cm)

Invaluable annual herb with a sweet, spicy flavour. Essential for bouquet garni.

3 Spearmint
Mentha spicata

H x S: 2ft (60cm) x Unlimited

Used for mint sauce and added to cooked vegetables. Said to relieve hiccoughs. Lilac flowers.

4 Parsley
Petroselinum crispum

H x S: 18 x 10in (45 x 25cm)

Biennial herb, rich in Vitamin C. Used widely as a garnish and to flavour sauces and butters. Raw parsley chewed is said to sweeten the breath.

5 Rosemary
Rosmarinus officinalis

H x S: 3 x 3ft (90 x 90cm)

Highly aromatic. Evergreen. Sprigs cooked with meat or poultry impart a lovely flavour. An infusion may be drunk as a soothing tea or used as a rinse for dark hair.

6 Sage
Salvia officinalis

H x S: 2 x 1ft (60 x 30cm)

Bushy shrub with bright mauve flowers, much loved by bees. Dried leaves used mostly in stuffings to serve with rich meats such as pork, duck or goose.

7 French Tarragon
Artemisia dracunculus

H x S: 2 x 1ft (60 x 30cm)

Perennial herb for flavouring salads and cooked meat dishes. Add to sauces to serve with vegetables. Steep in wine vinegar to use in french salad dressing.

8 Thyme
Thymus vulgaris

H x S: 6 x 10in (15 x 25cm)

Forms a low bush; spreads rapidly. Ingredient for bouquet garni. Use sparingly with soups, fish, stews and sauces. Add dried sprigs to pot-pourri.

H x S: Height x Spread

Most herbs prefer to be in a sunny position but the majority will thrive in any position.

HERBACEOUS & PERENNIAL PLANTS

1 Althaea
(Hollyhock)
Ht: 5ft (150cm) **FP:** July-Aug

Much loved cottage garden plant.

2 Agapanthus
(African Lily)
Ht: 3ft (90cm) **FP:** July-Sept

Clustered heads of handsome trumpet-like flowers.

**3 Aquilegia
'McKana Hybrids'**
(Columbine or Granny Bonnet)
Ht: 2½ft (75cm) **FP:** May-July

Large flowered variety with long spurs.

4 Aster (dwarf)
(Michaelmas Daisy)
Ht: 1½ft (45cm) **FP:** Sept-Oct

Valuable plant for the front of a border or bed. Many colours available.

5 Aster (tall)
(Michaelmas Daisy)
Ht: 3ft (90cm) **FP:** Sept-Oct

Good cut flower. Many colours available.

6 Astilbe
Ht: 2½ft (75cm) **FP:** June-Aug

Plume like heads. Likes rich moist soil. Water freely in hot dry weather.

7 Bergenia cordifolia
Ht: 1ft (30cm) **FP:** April-May

Useful for ground cover. Large leathery leaves.

8 Carnation *(Hardy Border)*
Ht: 1½ft (45cm) **FP:** July-Aug

Good for cutting. Many colours available.

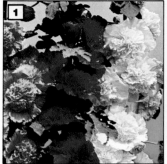

Ht: Height
FP: Flowering Period

Most herbaceous plants will tolerate light shade but prefer to grow in full sun. The above heights and flowering times are given as a general guide but depend upon area and growing conditions.

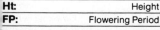

HERBACEOUS & PERENNIAL PLANTS

1 Chrysanthemum maximum 'Wirral Supreme'
Ht: 3ft (90cm) **FP:** July-Sept
Useful for floral arrangements.

2 Coreopsis grandiflora 'Mayfield Giant' *(Tickseed)*
Ht: 2½ft (75cm) **FP:** June-Sept
Deep yellow flowers on long stems.

3 Doronicum
Ht: 1½ft (45cm) **FP:** April-June
One of the earliest perennials to flower.

4 Dianthus *(Border Pinks)*
Ht: 1ft (30cm) **FP:** May-July
Summer favourites for the front of a border. Exquisite scent.

5 Lupin
Ht: 3ft (90cm) **FP:** June-July
Available in a wide range of colours. Cut off dead heads to prolong flowering.

6 Delphinium
Ht: 5ft (150cm) **FP:** June-Aug
Stately, showy spikes. First class plant for borders and island beds.

7 Campanula persicifolia
Ht: 3ft (90cm) **FP:** June-Aug
Striking bell-like flowers. Good cut flowers.

8 Achillea 'Cloth of Gold'
Ht: 3ft (90cm) **FP:** June-Aug
Flowers may be dried and used for winter decoration.

9 Chrysanthemum
Ht: 3½ft (105cm) **FP:** Aug-Oct
Many colours available.

10 Salvia superba 'East Friesland'
Ht: 1½ft (45cm) **FP:** June-Aug

11 Phlox paniculata
Ht: 2½ft (75cm) **FP:** July-Aug

12 Geranium *(Cranesbill)*
Ht: Various **FP:** May-Aug
Many colours and varieties available. Free-flowering and easy to grow.

Ht:	Height
FP:	Flowering Period

Most herbaceous plants will tolerate light shade but prefer to grow in full sun. The above heights and flowering times are given as a general guide but depend upon area and growing conditions.

HERBACEOUS & PERENNIAL PLANTS

1 Dianthus 'Highland Hybrids'
(Pinks)

Ht: 1ft (30cm) **FP:** June-July

Ideal for a rockery or between paving slabs.

2 Gaillardia 'Dazzler'
(Blanket Flower)

Ht: 2½ft (75cm) **FP:** June-Sept

Very free flowering.

3 Geum 'Lady Stratheden'
(Avens)

Ht: 2ft (60cm) **FP:** June-Aug

Double, yellow bowl-shaped flowers. Lovely, bright variety.

4 Geum 'Mrs. Bradshaw'

Ht: 2ft (60cm) **FP:** June-Aug

Easily grown border plant. Good for cutting.

5 Gypsophila paniculata

Ht: 3ft (90cm) **FP:** June-Aug

Cloud of tiny white flowers.

6 Helenium

Ht: 3ft (90cm) **FP:** July-Aug

Long lasting cut blooms. Lovely warm autumn colours.

7 Helleborus niger
(Christmas Rose)

Ht: 1ft (30cm) **FP:** Jan-March

Delicate white blooms. Protect opening buds.

8 Hosta fortunei 'Aurea marginata'
(Plantain Lily)

Ht: 2½ft (75cm) **FP:** June-Aug

Outstanding leaves. Good ground cover. Suitable for shady borders or poolside planting.

9 Iris germanica
(Bearded Iris)

Ht: 2½ft (75cm) **FP:** May-June

Sword-like foliage.

10 Kniphofia (Tritoma)
(Red Hot Poker)

Ht: 3ft (90cm) **FP:** July-Sept

Impressive plant of stately appearance.

11 Nepeta mussinii
(Catmint)

Ht: 1ft (30cm) **FP:** May-July

Excellent for carpeting the edge of perennial borders.

Ht:	Height
FP:	Flowering Period

Most herbaceous plants will tolerate light shade but prefer to grow in full sun. The above heights and flowering times are given as a general guide but depend upon area and growing conditions.

1 Paeonia lactiflora
(Peony)
Ht: 2½ft (75cm) **FP:** May-June

Magnificent flower heads. Dislikes transplanting, best left undisturbed.

2 Papaver nudicaule
(Iceland Poppy)
Ht: 1½ft (45cm) **FP:** June-July

Lovely poppy for cutting, gather in the morning before flowers are fully open.

3 Physalis franchetii
(Chinese Lantern)
Ht: 2½ft (75cm) **FP:** Sept-Nov

Invaluable for winter decoration.

4 Potentilla nepalensis 'Miss Willmott'
Ht: 2ft (60cm) **FP:** June-Sept

Very reliable.

5 Primula auricula
Ht: 6in (15cm) **FP:** April-June

Bright Spring flowers.

6 Primula denticulata
(Drumstick Primula)
Ht: 1ft (30cm) **FP:** Mar-May

Huge globose flower heads and tight rosettes of leaves.

7 Pyrethrum
Ht: 3ft (90cm) **FP:** May-June

Popular garden plant for a sunny border. Daisy-like flowers good for cutting.

8 Rudbeckia deamii
Ht: 3ft (90cm) **FP:** July-Sept

Long lasting displays. Good cut flower.

9 Scabiosa caucasica
Ht: 2½ft (75cm) **FP:** June-Sept

Profusion of pin-cushion like flower heads. Good cut flower.

10 Sedum 'Autumn Joy'
Ht: 2ft (60cm) **FP:** Aug-Oct

Outstanding plant.

Ht:	Height
FP:	Flowering Period

Most herbaceous plants will tolerate light shade but prefer to grow in full sun. The above heights and flowering times are given as a general guide but depend upon area and growing conditions.

SUMMER BEDDING PLANTS (please see overleaf for names of varieties)

SUMMER BEDDING PLANTS (For planting out in late Spring/early Summer)

Illustrated here and on the preceding page is a small selection from an ever-increasing range of varieties.

1	**Nemesia**
	○
2	**Tagetes**
	○ ☆
3	**Salvia splendens** (*Scarlet Sage*)
	○ ☆
4	**Aster**
	○ ☆
5	**Impatiens** (*Busy Lizzie*)
	◐ ☆
6	**Petunia**
	○ ☆
7	**Antirrhinum** (*Snapdragon*)
8	**Calendula** (*Pot Marigold*)
	○
9	**Dark Blue Lobelia**
	◐
10	**French Marigold**
	○ ☆
11	**Kochia** (*Burning Bush*)
	○ ☆
12	**Verbena**
	○ ☆
13	**Ageratum** (*Floss Flower*)
	○ ☆
14	**Mixed Lobelia**
	◐
15	**Alyssum**
	○
16	**Geranium**
	○ ☆

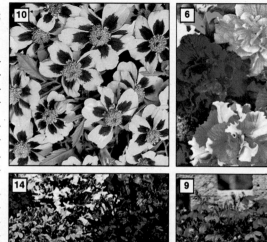

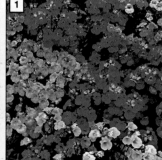

All bedding plants thrive in full sunlight, but those marked ◐ will also tolerate shadier conditions.

Bedding plants produce better results when watered and fed regularly throughout the summer.

Plants marked ☆ should not be planted out until all risk of frost has passed.

SUMMER BEDDING PLANTS (For planting out in late Spring/early Summer)

Illustrated here is a small selection from an ever-increasing range of varieties.

1 **Mesembryanthemum**
(Livingstone Daisy)
○

2 **Alyssum**
○

3 **Geranium**
○ ☆

4 **Verbena**
○ ☆

5 **Calcaeolaria**
(Slipper Flower)
○ ☆

6 **Viola 'Prince John'**
◑

7 **Aster 'Bouquet'**
(Michaelmas Daisy)
○ ☆

8 **Dahlia 'Mignon'**
○ ☆

9 **Phlox drummondii**
(Annual Phlox)
○ ☆

10 **Nicotiana affinis**
(Tobacco Plant)
○ ☆

11 **Fuchsia**
◑ ☆

12 **Antirrhinum**
(Snapdragon)
○

All bedding plants thrive in full sunlight, but those marked ◑ will also tolerate shadier conditions.

Bedding plants produce better results when watered and fed regularly throughout the summer.

Plants marked ☆ should not be planted out until all risk of frost has passed.

6

9

7

10

4

11

8

12

PATIO PLANTS

Containers should have adequate drainage. Regular watering is essential (daily in dry conditions). For best results feed weekly.

Suitable plants for containers and baskets are:–

Trailing/Upright Geranium

Trailing/Upright Fuchsia

Trailing Lobelia

Helichrysum

Nepeta

Trailing Petunias

Cascade Begonias

Dwarf Nasturtiums

A selection of other bedding plants can be added.

BULBS FOR SPRING PLANTING

1	**Gladiolus** *(Sword Lily)*	
	PD: 6"	
2	**Cactus Dahlia**	
	PD: 4-6" ☆	
3	**Dutch Iris**	
	PD: 3"	
4	**Crocosmia** *(Montbretia)*	
	PD: 3"	
5	**Acidanthera**	
	PD: 3"	
6	**Sparaxis** *(Harlequin Flower)*	
	PD: 2" ☆	
7	**Freesia**	
	PD: 2" ☆	
8	**Begonia**	
	PD: 1" ☆	
9	**Dahlia**	
	PD: 4-6" ☆	
10	**Chincherinchee** *(Ornithogalum)*	
	PD: 2"	
11	**Nerine**	
	PD: 3"	
12	**Lilium** *(Lily)*	
	PD: 5-6"	
13	**Anemone de Caen** *(Windflower)*	
	PD: 1-2"	
14	**Agapanthus** *(African Lily)*	
	PD: 2"	

Planted bulbs should be kept watered in dry weather.

PD Planting depth, measured from base of bulb.

Young shoots of plants marked ☆ should be protected from late frosts.

BULBS FOR AUTUMN PLANTING

Illustrated here is a small selection from a huge range of varieties readily available.

1 **Hybrid Tulip**
PD: 4-6"

2 **Dwarf Hybrid Tulip**
PD: 4-6"

3 **Double Early Hybrid Tulip**
PD: 4-6"

4 **Bi-colour Narcissus**
PD: 6"

5 **Short Cup Narcissus**
PD: 6"

6 **Trumpet Daffodil**
PD: 6"

7 **Dwarf Rockery Narcissus**
PD: 4"

8 **Hyacinth**
PD: 6"

9 **Grape Hyacinth**
(*Muscari*)
PD: 3"

10 **Pushkinia**
PD: 2"

11 **Dwarf Rockery Iris**
PD: 3"

12 **Rockery Crocus**
PD: 2"

13 **Dutch Crocus**
PD: 2"

14 **Scilla**
(*Squill*)
PD: 3"

15 **Crocus**
(*Naturalised*)

16 **Anemone Blanda**
with **Dwarf Narcissus**

17 Specially prepared **Hyacinth** for indoor flowering – mixed colours available.

PD: Planting depth, measured from base of bulb.

WINTER/SPRING FLOWERING BEDDING PLANTS

1 **Bellis perennis**
(Daisy)

2 **Cheiranthus cheiri**
(Wallflower)

3 **Myosotis alpestris**
(Forget-Me-Not)

4 **Viola**
(Universal Pansy)

5 **Dianthus barbatus**
(Sweet William)

These varieties, which should be planted in late Summer or early Autumn, can advantageously be planted in association with Spring-flowering bulbs, thus achieving maximum effect.

FRUIT

TOP FRUIT

APPLES

Most apples will produce fruit when planted alone but the crop will be greatly enhanced when two trees are planted together to aid pollination.

Generally, an early flowering variety will pollinate an early or a mid flowering variety.

A mid flowering variety will pollinate a mid, late or early flowering variety.

A late flowering variety will pollinate a late or a mid flowering variety.

1 Bramley's Seedling
C M S: Oct-Mar

2 Cox's Orange Pippin
D M S: Oct-Jan

3 Discovery
D M S: Aug-Oct

4 Egremont Russet
D E S: Oct-Dec

5 Golden Delicious
D L S: Oct-Mar

6 Grenadier
C M S: Sept-Oct

7 James Grieve
D E S: Sept-Oct

8 Laxton's Superb
D L S: Nov-Feb

9 Lord Lambourne
D E S: Oct-Nov

10 Worcester Pearmain
D L S: Sept-Oct

D:	Dessert
C:	Culinary
S:	Season of use
E:	Early Flowering
M:	Mid Flowering
L:	Late Flowering

TOP FRUIT

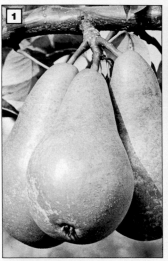

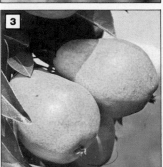

PEARS

Most pears will produce fruit when planted alone but the crop will be greatly enhanced when two trees are planted together to aid pollination. Select varieties with similar flowering times for best results.

1 **Conference**
D M H: Sept-Nov

2 **Doyenne du Comice**
D L H: Oct-Nov

3 **Williams Bon Chrêtien**
D M H: Sept

PLUMS

4 **Czar**
C SP H: Aug

5 **Damson**
C SP H: Sept

6 **Victoria**
D SP H: Late Aug

CHERRIES

7 **Early Rivers**
D H: June

8 **Merton Glory**
D H: Mid July

9 **Morello**
C SP H: Aug-Sept

10 **Stella**
D SP H: Late July

PEACH

11 **Peregrine**
SP H: Early Aug

D:	Dessert
C:	Culinary
SP:	Self Pollinator
H:	Harvest
M:	Mid Flowering
L:	Late Flowering

SOFT FRUIT

1 **Blackberry**
Fruits: Aug-Oct
Thornless varieties available.

2 **Black Currant**
Fruits: July-Aug

3 **Red Currant**
Fruits: July-Aug

4 **White Currant**
Fruits: July

5 **Gooseberry**
(green)
Fruits: June-July

6 **Gooseberry**
(pink)
Fruits: June-July

7 **Grape**
(white)
Fruits: Aug-Oct

8 **Grape**
(black)
Fruits: Aug-Oct

9 **Loganberry**
Fruits: July-Sept

10 **Raspberry**
Fruits: July-Sept

11 **Strawberry**
Fruits: Early Summer —
Late Autumn

12 **Tayberry**
Fruits: June

PLANTING INSTRUCTIONS

PLANTING A CONTAINER GROWN SHRUB OR ROSE

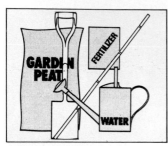

1. You will need
a. Spade
b. Watering can
c. A cane
d. Peat
e. General fertilizer

2. Ensure plant is still moist.

3. Mix together equal parts of moist peat and soil plus a little general fertilizer.

4. Dig hole large enough to hold the plant. Mix in prepared compost into base of hole.

5. To check if hole deep enough, place a cane across hole — the soil surface in the container should be about 2.5 cm (1") below the cane.

6. Remove container from plant and place in position.

7. Fill in remaining space with compost mixture and firm.

8. Leave a slight hollow around plant. Water well. If planting in dry weather keep plant regularly watered until it is established.

HOW TO PLANT AND STAKE A TREE

1. You will need
a. Spade
b. Fork
c. Stake
d. Two tree ties
e. A cane
f. Bucket of water
g. Peat
h. Bonemeal

2. Until planted, protect roots from wind and sun. If dry, soak in water for 5 minutes.

3. Remove the turf, leaving a circle of soil about 1.2m (4ft) across.

4. Dig hole large enough to accommodate outstretched roots and to the depth of the soil mark on the trunk. Fork over bottom of hole.

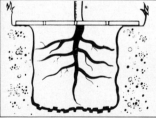

5. A cane placed across the top of the hole allows a check on planting level.

6. Mix peat in the base of the hole and drive stake in firmly before repositioning tree.

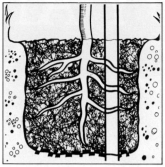

7. After positioning, fill in around the roots with a mixture of moist peat and soil to which a handful of bonemeal is added.
Gently shake tree up and down, allowing soil to settle amongst roots. Firm as you fill in.

8. A final firm with the heel.

9. Two tree ties are necessary, one just below the head of the tree and one about 45cm (1½ft) above soil level.

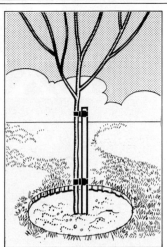

10. Tree correctly planted.

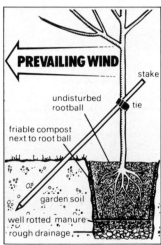

11. Method of staking container-grown tree or conifer to avoid breaking the rootball. Can also be used for tall shrubs, to prevent wind rocking.

BUY AND EXCHANGE
NATIONAL GARDEN GIFT TOKENS

National Garden Gift Tokens can be bought or exchanged at any H.T.A. shop, garden centre or nursery participating in the scheme. This means you can choose from over fourteen hundred outlets nationwide.   They may also be exchanged at Interflora Florist Shops.
Please ask your retailer for further details.

INDEX

ALPHABETICAL LIST OF BOTANICAL NAMES

INDEX

ALPHABETICAL LIST OF COMMON NAMES

INDEX